Chapter 1: Trip to the Seaside 2

Chapter 2: Paddling and Crabs .... page 8

Chapter 3: Building Sandcastles .... page 14

Chapter 4: Crazy Golf and Ice-Cream .... page 20

Chapter 5: The Presents .... page 25

Written by Adam and Charlotte Guillain

Chapter 1: Trip to the Seaside!

One sunny day in the holidays, Rav and Asha were playing in Tess and Finn's garden.

Finn was splashing in the paddling pool with his little brother, Dylan.

"This is nearly as good as paddling in the sea!" said Finn.

"I've never been to the seaside," said Rav.

What's it like?

Tess and Finn's dad smiled. "The seaside's great," he told Rav. "I grew up near the coast in Wales. We spent all our summers playing on the beach."

When the friends went to play on the swings, Mr Harrison made a phone call.

When they came back from the play area, Asha's dad and Rav's parents were waiting inside.

"How would you all like to go to the seaside tomorrow?" asked Mr Harrison.

Rav's eyes widened. "Can I go?" he asked his mum.

"Of course," she said, "it's all arranged."

"Thank you!" said Rav and Asha, jumping up and down.

The next day, the four friends got up early for their journey to Wales.

Rav's dad handed him a bag. "There's a bucket and spade and some spending money in here," he said.

"Thanks!" said Rav. "I can't wait to paddle and make sandcastles and eat ice-creams. And I'll bring you back something," he told his sister, Alpa.

They all jumped into Mr Harrison's car and waved goodbye to their families. Mr Harrison beeped the horn as they turned into the road and drove away. Soon they were whizzing out of the city and shooting past fields and woods.

"Let's play 'I spy'," suggested Finn, looking out of the window.

"It's such a long way!" groaned Tess later, fidgeting in her seat.

"Look out of the window as we go round the bend," said her dad, his eyes shining.

They all stared and then cheered as the car swung into a bay.

"The sea!" shouted Rav.

We're here!

Chapter 2: Paddling and Crabs

They parked the car and everyone got out and stretched. Mr Harrison took a deep breath and opened his arms. "Smell that sea air!" he said. "Race you to the beach!" he added, setting off down the sandy path.

The four friends ran down to the beach and pulled off their shoes and socks.

"Who wants to paddle?" yelled Finn, rolling up his trousers.

"Me!" said Rav. They ran towards the sea.

"Argh! It's so cold!" squealed Asha, as the gentle waves lapped over her toes.

"Can we make sandcastles now?" asked Rav.

"We've only just started paddling!" said Tess with a laugh.

"Let's write our names in the sand," said Tess.

"I've done mine!" shouted Rav. "Let's build sandcastles!"

But Finn was racing away. "Look! A crab!" he yelled, pointing at a creature scuttling up the beach.

"Where's it going?" asked Asha.

"It's heading towards those rock pools," said Tess. "Come on!"

They clambered over the slippery rocks after the crab. It plopped into a small pool of water and they crouched down to watch it.

"Ooh, that starfish is so pretty," gasped Asha, watching the bright orange star sway in the water.

Rav stared into the pool. "That shell's moving!" he cried.

Tess laughed. "It's a hermit crab," she told Rav. "It hasn't got a hard shell like other crabs so it hides inside a seashell."

"Can we take it home?" asked Asha.

"No," said Finn. "Dad says we have to put everything back on the beach where we found it."

Rav was already picking his way through the rocks back to the sand. "It's got to be time to make sandcastles now!"

Tess gently placed the hermit crab back in the pool. They raced up the beach after Rav, who was pulling his bucket and spade out of his bag.

Chapter 3: Building Sandcastles

"Watch where you're throwing that sand!" said Mr Harrison, as everyone built their sandcastles. "It's landing right in the middle of my book!" he added, brushing the sand away.

"I want to make at least ten!" thought Rav, as he began filling his bucket again.

Asha made a big perfect, sandcastle. "I'm going to decorate them!" she said, running off to find shells.

"My sandcastles keep collapsing," muttered Rav.

"You're making them too fast," said Tess, as she pressed sand into her bucket.

"Don't forget to dig a moat," called Finn.

"Why?" asked Rav.

"When the tide comes in, it will fill with water," Finn explained.

Copying Finn, Rav dug a moat around his sandcastles quickly, then started building even more.

"Wow, look at this!" Asha cried, holding up a small piece of driftwood. "It looks like a reindeer!"

"Put it on top of the castle!" said Tess.

"Let me take a photo," said Mr Harrison.

"But I'm not ready!" thought Rav, as they stood by their sandcastles and the camera clicked.

Mr Harrison got out the picnic. "Lunchtime!" he said.

Rav gulped down his sandwiches while the others chatted. "I want to make some more sandcastles," he thought. "And eat ice-creams!"

"Here comes the tide!" shouted Tess. Soon the moats had filled with water.

"Quick!" said her dad. "Time to move off the beach!"

Rav looked at the sandcastles longingly. "They'll disappear soon!"

"You could take the driftwood to remember them," said Asha.

"Yes," said Mr Harrison. "But we should leave the shells and pebbles."

They scrambled up the beach and watched as the tide gradually washed over their sandcastles.

"I think that was my best ever sandcastle," sighed Finn.

"I wanted to make some more," said Rav. "None of mine were as good as yours!"

"I know what will cheer you up," said Mr Harrison.

Chapter 4: Crazy Golf and Ice-Cream

Mr Harrison led them along the beach towards a red and white hut.

"Ice-creams?" asked Rav hopefully. But Mr Harrison came back with golf clubs and coloured balls.

"Time for a game of crazy golf," he said. "If there's time, we can have an ice-cream afterwards!"

They took it in turns to hit the balls around the course.

"Oops, sorry, Tess," said Asha, as her ball knocked Tess's into a hole.

"I don't mind!" said Tess with a laugh.

"Hurry up!" said Rav, thinking about ice-creams.

Rav rushed so much he kept hitting the ball too hard and missing the hole. As he handed in his golf club, he saw Mr Harrison looking at his watch.

"I think it's time to go home," Mr Harrison said.

"Go home?" cried Rav. "But we haven't done everything! What about ice-creams?"

"I'm not sure …" said Mr Harrison.

Rav reached into his bag. "What if I buy them for everyone?"

Finn laughed. "You must really want an ice-cream!"

"I do," Rav said, nodding his head quickly. "We can't go to the seaside without having an ice-cream!"

Soon they were sitting on the cliff top licking delicious ice-creams and looking out at the turquoise sea.

"It's been such a great day," sighed Asha.

"Now it really is time to go," said Mr Harrison, looking at his watch again.

Chapter 5: The Presents

The sun was setting when they reached the city. Asha was asleep and Tess was yawning and stretching. Finn was sitting in the front seat, chatting quietly with his dad. As the car pulled into Comet Street, Rav saw his family waiting outside the flats and gasped.

"I forgot to get a present for Alpa!" cried Rav.

Asha was uncurling and rubbing her eyes. "You could give her the reindeer," she suggested. Rav felt a lump in his throat.

"Yes, I could," he sighed, getting out of the car.

Everyone was chattering excitedly as they headed into the flats and thanked Mr Harrison.

"I brought you this from the beach," said Rav, handing his little sister the piece of driftwood.

"Thank you!" cried Alpa, giving Rav a hug.

The next morning, Rav lay in bed remembering the trip.

"I wish I could have kept the driftwood for my holiday challenge," he thought, looking at the empty folder Mrs Knight had given him. Their teacher had asked the class to collect things over the summer.

"I've got nothing to remember the seaside. I shouldn't have rushed so much," Rav thought sadly.

As Rav ate his breakfast, there was a knock on the door. Tess and Finn rushed in.

"Our dad wanted you to have this photo from yesterday," said Finn as Tess held out the picture. "It's a souvenir of our day at the beach."

"Thanks," said Rav, grinning at the photo. "It's perfect!"

At the Seaside

What other things will the Comet Street Kids collect
for their holiday challenge? Read the other books
in this band to find out!

At the Seaside

The Summer Fete

The Laughing Kookaburra

Help the Vikings

The Sleepover

Asteroid Alarm!

Talk about the story

Answer the questions:

1 Where did Tess and Finn's dad grow up?

2 What game did they play on the way to the seaside?

3 What was the first activity the friends did at the seaside?

4 What does the word 'lapped' mean (page 9)?

5 Why was Rav so eager to make sandcastles?

6 Can you describe what happened at the end when Rav didn't have anything for his sister?

7 Why was it okay for Rav to take the driftwood but not the crab?

8 Have you ever been to the seaside? What did you do there?

Can you retell the story using your own words?